UNCOMMON
Word Puzzles
for the Creative Thinker

D1472881

Rita Norr & Audrey Tumbarello

Sterling Publishing Co., Inc.
New York

Edited by Jeanette Green

3   5   7   9   10   8   6   4   2

Published by Sterling Publishing Company, Inc.
387 Park Avenue South, New York, N.Y. 10016
© 1997 by Rita Norr and Audrey Tumbarello
Distributed in Canada by Sterling Publishing
℅ Canadian Manda Group, One Atlantic Avenue, Suite 105
Toronto, Ontario, Canada M6K 3E7
Distributed in Great Britain and Europe by Cassell PLC
Wellington House, 125 Strand, London WC2R 0BB, England
Distributed in Australia by Capricorn Link (Australia) Pty Ltd.
P.O. Box 6651, Baulkham Hills, Business Centre, NSW 2153, Australia

Sterling   ISBN 0-8069-8118-0

Contents

Anagram and Hook Riddles

Anagrammatize

Anagrammatize means to rearrange letters to discover a hidden message. Find words that are anagrams of each other to discover the answers to these riddles. The number of blanks indicates the number of letters in the anagrammed words.

Example: Sneaky silverware checker? <u>SPOON</u> <u>SNOOP</u>

1. Backpackers yell?

   — — — — — — — — — — — —

2. Improper escort?

   — — — — — — — — — — — —

3. News from the luggage handler?

   — — — — — — — — — — — —

4. Train stations for tyrants?

   — — — — — — — — — — — —

5. Heavy tipsters?

   — — — — — — — — — —

6. Environmentally sound writing style?

   — — — — — — — — — —

7. Minnie's pouts?

   — — — — — — — — — —

8. Discovered Swiss cheese dip?

   — — — — — — — — — —

9. Pale chump!

   — — — — — — — — — —

10. Mean stomach ailment?

    — — — — — — — — — —

Anagrammatize II

Use the fanciful clues below to help find two anagrams, each using *all* the letters in the accompanying letter sets that solve the riddle.

Example: Russian clerical gear?   A C C K O S S
        <u>COSSACK</u> <u>CASSOCK</u>

1. An editor?   A C E H P R T

   _____   _____

2. Exam seating?   E E E S T T

   _____   _____

3. Cents off a little something?   C N O O P S U

   _____   _____

4. Risqué wedding ceremony?   A B D I L R

   _____   _____

5. Italian aviatrix?   A G I N O R S

   _____   _____

6. Undertaker job?   C E O P R S S

   _____   _____

7. Shoplifting drummer?   B G I N O O S T

   _____   _____

8. The look of love?   A D E E M N O R

   _____   _____

9. Receptacle for shredded pro-Nazi papers?
   B D I N S T U

   _____   _____

10. Shorter secondary social group?   B B E I R S T U

   _____   _____

Anagrammatize III

Use the fanciful clues below to help find two anagrams, each using *all* the letters in the accompanying letter sets that solve the riddle.

Example: Russian clerical gear?   A C C K O S S
          <u>COSSACK</u> <u>CASSOCK</u>

1. End of the line for Desire?   A E I L M N R T

   _____   _____

2. Food for Indian navy?   C E I R R S U

   _____   _____

3. Shortened exam?   D E I M M R T

   _____   _____

4. Vilest snobberies?   E I I L M S S T

   _____   _____

5. Dreamiest feelings?   E I M N O O S T

   _____   _____

6. Old West soup?   C D E H O R W

   _____   _____

7. Eccentric grill?   A B E I R R Z

   _____   _____

8. Battling bird?   A B E L R R W

   _____   _____

9. Heraldic crest for a sexpot?   A A M N P R T

   _____   _____

10. Amusement park bully?   A F F I N R U

    _____   _____

ANAGRAMMATIZE IV

Use the fanciful clues below to help find two anagrams, each using *all* the letters in the accompanying
letter sets that solve the riddle.

Example: Russian clerical gear?   A C C K O S S
<u>COSSACK</u> <u>CASSOCK</u>

1. Anorexic's meal?   D E E F I G N

   _____   _____

2. Fear of flying?   E I J R T T

   _____   _____

3. Evocative verse?   D E E L N O R T

   _____   _____

4. Most commonplace sallies?   E I O P R S S T

   _____   _____

5. Oddballs' tranquilizer?   A D E E I S T V

   _____,   _____

6. Job for colonial housewife?   A C G H I N P T

   _____   _____

7. Detective dance?   E H L S T U

   _____   _____

8. Stolen pastry?   D E L R S T U

   _____   _____

9. Procrastinating worship?   A D I L O R T Y

   _____   _____

10. Adolf stamps?   A E G O P S T

    _____   _____

ANAGRAMMATIZE V

Use the fanciful clues below to help find two anagrams, each using *all* the letters in the accompanying letter sets that solve the riddle.

Example: Russian clerical gear?   A C C K O S S
             <u>COSSACK</u> <u>CASSOCK</u>

1. Multi-faceted family members?   A E E I L R S T V

   _____   _____

2. Went on without attention?   C D E I N N O T U

   _____   _____

3. Bad luck for the auto repairman?
A C C E H I M N S

   _____,__   _____

4. Manly misrepresentations?   A C E I L M N S U

   _____   _____

5. Underwear chooser?   C E E L O R S T

   _____   _____

6. Expeditious contrariness?   A E G I I M N S T V

   _____   _____

7. *Very* high speed drums?   C E I N O P R S S U

   _____   _____

8. Required banalities?   A D E I L P S T T U

   _____   _____

9. Smuttier storm?   A C E H I N R R U

   _____   _____

10. What a chiropractor may be heard doing?
A E G I L M N N T

   _____   _____

Anagrammatize VI

Use the fanciful clues below to help find two anagrams, each using *all* the letters in the accompanying letter sets that solve the riddle.

Example: Russian clerical gear?   A C C K O S S
          <u>COSSACK</u> <u>CASSOCK</u>

1. Fellow sailors?   A E H I M P S S T

   _____   _____

2. Climber count?   A E E I M N N O R T U

   _____   _____

3. Take back the coffees?   E E O P R S S S S

   _____   _____

4. Itinerant rain or snow?   A C E E I I P P R T T

   _____   _____

5. Talk about preservation?
   A C E I N N O O R S T V

   _____   _____

6. Instill fear in the carouser?   E E I O R R R S T

   _____   _____

7. Football player's vivid memory?
   A A B C F H K L S

   _____,__   _____

8. Continuing attractiveness?   E E I N P R S S T T

   _____   _____

9. Naughty wall hangings?   A E E I P R S S T T

   _____   _____

10. Eye doctor's rival?   C E I M O O P R T T

    _____   _____

DOUBLE TAKE

Use each set of letters below *twice* to create a word and a common phrase. Both the word and the phrase each must use all the letters. The clues, though silly, will help.

Example: Before bureaucracy?   A D E E P R T
 <u>PREDATE</u> <u>RED</u> <u>TAPE</u>

1. Direct phone lines to cow barn?   E H I L N O S T

   — — — — — — — —   — — —   — — — — —

2. Senior mathematician's propositions?
   E E H M O R S T

   — — — —   — — — —   — — — — — — —

3. Close-call study groups?   A E I M N R S S

   — — — — - — — — —   — — — — — — — —

4. Totally failed bean dish?   A C E L O S S T U

   — — — — - — — — — —

   — — — — — — — — —

5. More heavenly outdoor movie?   D E I I N R V

   — — — — — — —   — — — — — - — —

6. Wranglers' ready money payment?
   A C D H N O S W

   — — — —   — — — — '   — — — —   — — — —

7. What psychic's 800 number can do!
   E E F L L O R T

   — — — — — — — —   — — — —   — — — —

8. Legal proceeding involving some tapes?
   A C E E S S T T

   — — — — — — — —   — — — —   — — — —

9. Hotel registration for coward?   C C E H I K N

   _ _ _ _ _ _ _   _ _ _ _ _‑_ _

10. Old salts' measured medicines?   A D E G O S S

    _ _ _　_ _ _ _'   _ _ _ _ _ _ _ _

11. Obstructionist paid daily?   D E E I M P R

    _ _ _   _ _ _ _   _ _ _ _ _ _ _

12. Procrastinator's finery?   A A D G G L R S

    _ _ _ _ _ _ _'_   _ _ _ _   _ _ _ _

13. Stiffest winter athlete?   A C E E I K R S T

    _ _ _ _ _ _ _ _ _   _ _ _
    _ _ _ _ _ _

14. Once popular wailing spirit?   A B E E H N S

    _ _ _ _ _ _ _   _ _ _‑_ _ _ _

15. Forceful entry to steal a furry rug?
    A B E I K N R S

    _ _ _ _ _ _ _ _   _ _ _ _ _‑_ _

16. Gear for the "expert" flasher?
    A C C E H N O R T T

    _ _ _ _ _ _ _ _ _ _   _ _ _ _ _ _
    _ _ _ _

HOOK SHOTS

Each word below can be made into a new word by adding *only one* letter to the front of the word. When you find the letters, anagram them to find the answer to the riddle. Some use British spelling.

1. Useless timepiece?

   __ Q U I P P E D   __ A L L I A N C E
   __ S L A N D E R   __ E V E R T
   __ L A Y O F F   __ L I K E N E S S
   __ U N L I T   __ E I T H E R
   __ N E A T E N   __ A P P L E
   __ A G E L E S S   __ T R O P H I E S
   __ E M E S I S   __ I O N I Z E

   — — — — — — — — — — — —

2. Semiprofessional dog or cat?

   __ B A S E M E N T   __ M O U N T E D
   __ M E R G E N C E   __ R E V I E W
   __ E L A P S E   __ H E R E A F T E R
   __ R E S E R V E

   — — — — — —

3. Kangaroo's favorite game?

   __ W I N N I N G   __ D O U R
   __ R A V I N G S   __ A L O E S
   __ T I T I S   __ E L E C T
   __ A I R I E R   __ H I D I N G
   __ R O O F

   — — — — — — —

4. Description of an angry kangaroo?

__ H O S T   __ V I E D
__ O V A   __ L U C K Y
__ A R S O N   __ A I R B R U S H
__ A S C O T   __ R I V E R
__ S P I R E   __ P I N I O N E D

— — — — — — — — — —

5. Footwear for a plunderer?

__ E R R O R   __ R A L L Y
__ A C T O R   __ L A P S E
__ T I F F   __ E A G L E
__ L I C I T   __ Z O N E
__ E V E R Y

— — — — — — — —

6. The Devil's pet?

__ R U M P L E   __ M I G R A N T
__ A R M L E S S   __ I T E R A T E
__ A N G U I S H   __ W E E D I E R
__ T H E I S T

— — — — — — —

7. Job of the kangaroo babysitter?

__ O V E R T   __ O K A Y
__ I W I S   __ R A T I O N
__ F L O A T   __ R O B I N G
__ A I R L I N E   __ H O R N L I K E
__ O L D I S H   __ H E L M
__ N U M E R A T E

— — — — — — — — — — —

8. What do you call a game they don't let you play?

   __ H A S T E   __ A M E N T
   __ N A V E   __ R O A D S I D E
   __ B R O A D   __ V A I L
   __ I M I T A B L E   __ L E A K
   __ A P S E

   — — — — — — — — —

9. A cooking container for a crazy person?

   __ R O C K E R Y   __ H O N E Y
   __ S T E R O I D   __ N E E D
   __ E N F O L D   __ A R O U S E
   __ E V I L E R   __ C A R I N A

   — — — — — — — —

10. Baby kangaroo's best friend?

   __ R A N G Y   __ R E S U M E
   __ B A S E M E N T   __ S P O U S E
   __ E G G   __ O V E R L Y
   __ A R G O N

   — — —   — — — —

CATEGORY ANAGRAMS

COMMON SENSE

Unscramble each letter set below, and then determine the common theme or category. Some are proper nouns and some sets contain multiple anagrams, but only one fits the category. Finding the theme will help you decipher the more difficult words.

1. a. CLOPRSTU
   b. AEIKMNPRRT
   c. ACINOORSTT
   d. ACEIMRST
   e. AEINPRT

Category _____

2. a. AEGMS
   b. EELOPP
   c. AGLMORU
   d. EGMROUT
   e. EEEENNTSV

Category _____

3. a. ACST
   b. AHIR
   c. AEHLMT
   d. ACELORSU
   e. AEGINNOT

Category _____

4. a. ACCENR
   b. AEIRS
   c. GIORV
   d. AAIQRSUU
   e. CEIPSS

Category _____

5. a. EFIL
   b. CEEHIORS
   c. AAELMOT
   d. AAGLNOR
   e. AEEHISTW

Category _____

6. a. EEEKPR
   b. ACEGS
   c. AEEHLNPT
   d. AEFFGIR
   e. ADELOPR

Category _____

7. a. ABEILLR
   b. ACIILOSST
   c. CIMMNOSTU
   d. ACCDEIMORT
   e. ABCEILNPRU

Category _____

8. a. ACELMR
   b. CCDNOOR
   c. ACCGHIO
   d. ACDEELLNV
   e. ACEHLNORST

Category _____

COMMON SENSE II

1. a. ACEHLNORST
   b. EKMNOY
   c. AEQRSU
   d. AKLOP
   e. ACGNO

Category _____

2. a. AERSWY
   b. AEHRRT
   c. AEENORRS
   d. ABKORW
   e. AELRSTW

Category _____

3. a. CDEEIRRRSVW
   b. AAAHMNNTT
   c. AIIMNRT
   d. EGILMT
   e. AADEELNRX

Category _____

4. a. FHIS
   b. AEHRST
   c. BDEGIR
   d. CEHILNOP
   e. AEIILORST

Category _____

5. a. BCHORST
   b. BEIQSU
   c. CEMMNOOS
   d. BILLNOOU
   e. EEPRU

Category _____

6. a. DIMOSW
   b. CIINORS
   c. EEY
   d. AEFLS
   e. BCDIIPSU

Category _____

7. a. DHILNOPS
   b. BCOOSWY
   c. ACEKPRS
   d. ADEIRRS
   e. EEELRSST

Category _____

8. a. ENOPRTW
   b. ACELM
   c. INNOSTW
   d. ABLMOORR
   e. AELMS

Category _____

9. a. GMU
   b. EHNOY
   c. AIINOSSTTU
   d. EGLU
   e. ILLLOOPP

Category _____

10. a. ACIMNOR
    b. AFIKLNNR
    c. DEINOS
    d. FLNOTU
    e. EHINTWY

Category _____

COMMON SENSE III

1. a. ACHIRTY
   b. CNOOTT
   c. ABCEH
   d. EINNST
   e. BBERRU
Category _____

2. a. EEEINPRRST
   b. CKOPS
   c. CEHKOV
   d. COSTTY
   e. GIKLNNOS
Category _____

3. a. ABDEILMN
   b. ABFILU
   c. ADIRSU
   d. AAELLPT
   e. EHMRSUU
Category _____

4. a. EILRSV
   b. EGGIRRT
   c. AEILSS
   d. EFILPPR
   e. IMORRS
Category _____

5. a. ADNS
   b. ALNO
   c. AADEEHHMMR
   d. AKMO
   e. EGIRT
Category _____

6. a. DHIINOU
   b. EILMNR
   c. ABCEKLNOST
   d. EGHINNN
   e. CDEEFILOPPR
Category _____

7. a. CNOOPPR
   b. AERST
   c. AAAGIMRRT
   d. ACENO
   e. EELPRSTZ
Category _____

8. a. AMNORS
   b. ACHINNOTW
   c. AABCERT
   d. AHMPOOS
   e. AEILN
Category _____

9. a. ABLLMOOR
   b. ABCEIOR
   c. ABELLT
   d. DEMNOR
   e. CNORTUY
Category _____

10. a. ADEELNRV
    b. AEGNOOR
    c. AACEGILN
    d. ACDEIONRR
    e. AAGNORRT
Category _____

COMMON SENSE IV

1. a. CEEFLORRT
   b. BELORST
   c. BNNRSUU
   d. AACDILNR
   e. GHILTS
Category _____

2. a. AEHMSTTY
   b. ADDIMNO
   c. AOPTZ
   d. AEHIPPRS
   e. ADEELMR
Category _____

3. a. AAEHRRT
   b. BDEGHILNR
   c. GHIRTW
   d. GEORRS
   e. CDEEHKLO
Category _____

4. a. CDKOOOSTW
   b. ADEFGILR
   c. ADDGOOW
   d. ACEINORV
   e. ACHTY
Category _____

5. a. AEHLZ
   b. AAAACDIMM
   c. ADLMNO
   d. ACHIIOPST
   e. CHIOKRY
Category _____

6. a. CEFHNR
   b. AAIILNT
   c. AMOTZ
   d. CEEIKLMNPPRU
   e. EHITW
Category _____

7. a. AL AADGIRU
   b. DELLSU
   c. BBHOY
   d. AGLNO
   e. DEEKNNY
Category _____

8. a. AGMMNU
   b. DEIINORS
   c. CDFKOORR
   d. CBLMOOU
   e. EINNNOST
Category _____

9. a. CCEEILRT
   b. EEHLW
   c. DFGILON
   d. GHHI
   e. EGLNOU
Category _____

10. a. EEPPPR
    b. HRTU
    c. DEILLOOTT
    d. GIILNNOSTV
    e. KLYEJL
Category _____

1. a. CEHHHKRSUV
    b. AILNST
    c. EILNN
    d. BEEHNRVZ
    e. ABCEGHORV
Category _____

2. a. AACRT
    b. AGIKLMOR
    c. EEGHINNPTWY
    d. DNOPU
    e. AGINR
Category _____

3. a. ACEENPRRT
    b. EHITW
    c. ADEHPRS
    d. ADILNR
    e. ELLLOV
Category _____

4. a. EHINOR
    b. AAAIJMNRU
    c. AHHHISS
    d. IMOPU
    e. ACEEILMNS
Category _____

5. a. AEGNTYZ
    b. AEHMST
    c. ADJNOR
    d. AAMNOZ
    e. EEINS
Category _____

6. a. IIMMN
    b. ADMR
    c. INPT
    d. AGLLNO
    e. EILRT
Category _____

7. a. AABCITX
    b. ELMNO
    c. ACDORW
    d. AACNRY
    e. AAABNN
Category _____

8. a. CEIINOS
    b. AACERS
    c. ADFLORW
    d. ACHINPS
    e. ACELLOSW
Category _____

9. a. EGOOS
    b. AEGT
    c. DEILO
    d. ELRU
    e. EGLOVS
Category _____

10. a. ANNSTU
    b. EILOV
    c. MOORT
    d. AEUNPT
    e. AEFFLORSW
Category _____

TOUGH ANAGRAMS AND BEYOND

STRETCHING YOUR MIND

Anagram each set of five letters below to find the only word possible using all the letters. Then add the given letter and *re-anagram* to find a six-letter word *that does not end in "S"*.

Examples: E N O O Z   O Z O N E
           + S =   S N O O Z E

1. A B O R X _____ + C = _____

2. A C N O P _____ + Y = _____

3. O P T U Y _____ + A = _____

4. I I S T V _____ + B = _____

5. B C I K R _____ + E = _____

6. D E R R U _____ + M = _____

7. C C K L O _____ + E = _____

8. I N P P U _____ + G = _____

9. H I N O R _____ + E = _____

10. G I I L V _____ + N = _____

11. A A L N V _____ + D = _____

12. H I S S U _____ + Q = _____

13. I I L M T _____ + S = _____

14. A E S T U _____ + L = _____

*15. H L M P Y _____ + U = _____

*16. H M R R Y _____ + E = _____

*Expert level

24

Stretching Your Mind II

Anagram each set of seven letters below to find the only word possible using all the letters. Then add the given letter and *re-anagram* to find an eight-letter word.

Example: D E I O P R S   <u>P E R I O D S</u>
      +   M   = <u>P R O M I S E D</u>

1. A E E K R S T _____ + D = _____

2. E G I L O R S _____ + S = _____

3. A E G H R S T _____ + O = _____

4. A C D E O S T _____ + C = _____

5. E E O R R S T _____ + U = _____

6. D E I L L O S _____ + C = _____

7. A I N R S T T _____ + M = _____

8. E I L O P R S _____ + F = _____

9. A D E I N T T _____ + A = _____

10. C D E N O R S _____ + I = _____

11. A B G I N S T _____ + D = _____

12. D E I O R S S _____ + L = _____

13. A H I N R S T _____ + G = _____

14. A D E I M R T _____ + O = _____

15. D E H I R S T _____ + T = _____

16. A E E I M N S _____ + X = _____

BLACK AND WHITE

It's all here in black and white, or is it? See if you can anagram the letters in WHITE or BLACK with the given word to find a new word. You must use all the letters.

Example: W H I T E + D A R N S
          = H A N D W R I T E S

1. W H I T E + C R Y = _____

2. W H I T E + S O R E = _____

3. W H I T E + E S S = _____

4. W H I T E + S E C = _____

5. W H I T E + H E R = _____

6. W H I T E + R A D S = _____

7. W H I T E + T E N T = _____

8. W H I T E + S A C K = _____

9. W H I T E + G L E N S = _____

10. B L A C K + P E A = _____

11. B L A C K + S I D E = _____

12. B L A C K + D O O R = _____

13. B L A C K + S A M E = _____

14. B L A C K + D R I B = _____

15. B L A C K + M A C E = _____

16. B L A C K + O D E = _____

17. B L A C K + O L E = _____

ANAGRAM ANNIE

Anagram Annie loves to play the anagram game and prides herself on being a pro at stealing other players' eight-letter words with only one letter. First, anagram the given set of letters to find the only eight-letter word. Next, add the given letter and anagram to find the only nine-letter word.

Example: A E H I R S T Y = <u>H Y S T E R I A</u>
+ L = <u>H A I R S T Y L E</u>

1. A C E I L N R T _____ + Y _____

2. A E I M P R S T _____ + N _____

3. A D E I N P R S _____ + P _____

4. A E I M N R T U _____ + I _____

5. A B E I I N R S _____ + T _____

6. A E E I N N T V _____ + L _____

7. A B E I K N S T _____ + E _____

8. A E I M N R S Y _____ + H _____

9. A E I K M N S T _____ + O _____

10. A C E I R S T Z _____ + O _____

11. A D D E I N S T _____ + L _____

12. A E E I M M N T _____ + C _____

13. A C E I N O R S _____ + X _____

14. A E G I N R S V _____ + H _____

15. A B E I R S T V _____ + L _____

ANAGRAM ANNIE II

1. E I L N N O S T _____ + G _____
2. E I N O R S U V _____ + L _____
3. E E I M N O R S _____ + Z _____
4. A E F I I R S T _____ + P _____
5. D E I M N O S T _____ + W _____
6. E I N O Q S T U _____ + T _____
7. E I N O P R S V _____ + C _____
8. D E G I L N O S _____ + S _____
9. A C C D E I R T _____ + P _____
10. A C E H I L N T _____ + C _____
11. A C D E O P R S _____ + Y _____
12. B E I O R S T Y _____ + V _____
13. A E G I L N O S _____ + D _____
14. E E I N R S T Y _____ + A _____
15. C E I M N R S T _____ + O _____
16. A E N N O R S T _____ + K _____
17. A E F M N R S T _____ + G _____
18. A E E N R S T U _____ + M _____
19. A E I L L N R Y _____ + T _____
20. E E I L L N O R _____ + B _____

Anagram PhD

Get your word PhD with this tough anagram challenge! Below are twenty-six sets of eight letters, plus a *question mark* which can represent any letter. Each set forms only one nine-letter word *starting with the letter "P"*, and in each word *the question mark represents a different letter of the alphabet.* Cross out the letters as you use them.

All of the words are common, although they may be hard to find. Some are compound words. If you have letter tiles from any word game such as Scrabble® or anagrams, shuffle them to help you solve the puzzle.

A B C D E F G H I J K L M
N O P Q R S T U V W X Y Z

1. A C E E L O P T ? _____

2. E I I N O P R T ? _____

3. A C E N P T U U ? _____

4. A C H K O P R T ? _____

5. A C G G I K P Y ? _____

6. A C E G N N P R ? _____

7. E E G I I L P R ? _____

8. H O O O P P T Y ? _____

9. A E I L L P R U ? _____

10. A F I N P R T Y ? _____

11. I I M O P R T Y ? _____

12. E I N O P R T Z ? _____

13. E H I P S S U Y? _____

14. C H I K O P R T? _____

15. A A I L P R S Y? _____

16. A A A G H P R R? _____

17. A E E L N P P P? _____

18. C C I O P S T Y? _____

19. A F I L L P U Y? _____

20. E E I L P R V Z? _____

21. E H N P R R S U? _____

22. C H I O P P R T? _____

23. A A N O P R T U? _____

24. E E P R R R S U? _____

25. A E H M P P S T? _____

26. A A E N O P R T? _____

ANAGRAM PhD II

Get your word PhD with this tough anagram challenge! Below are twenty-four sets of eight letters, plus a *question mark* which can represent any letter except "J" and "Q", missing in the letter chart. Each set forms only one nine-letter word *starting with the letter "H"*, and in each word *the question mark represents a different letter of the alphabet.* Cross out the letters as you use them.

A B C D E F G H I K L M
N O P R S T U V W X Y Z

1. C E H I O R T Y ? _____

2. E H M N O O R W ? _____

3. C H O O O P R S ? _____

4. B C E H M N O O ? _____

5. H I I L L L L Y ? _____

6. A A A D H H P R ? _____

7. B D E E H I I R ? _____

8. A C D E H O R R ? _____

9. A C H I I L M O ? _____

10. A B E G H N R R ? _____

11. A C D E E H N Y ? _____

12. E H I L M O R S ? _____

13. E E H I O S U W ? _____

14. A D H I K N O R ? _____

15. A A E G H L N O ? _____

16. A H I I O S S T ? _____

17. A A B D E H L N ? _____

18. A E H I N O R Z ? _____

19. H I N O P T T Y ? _____

20. A C H L O O S T ? _____

21. C E H H I R R Y ? _____

22. A H I I N O R S ? _____

23. A B E H R R T U ? _____

24. C E H H I I T K ? _____

ANAGRAM PhD III

Get your word PhD with this tough anagram challenge! Below are twenty-five sets of eight letters, plus a *question mark* which can represent any letter except "J", missing in the letter chart. Each set forms only one nine-letter word *starting with the letter "D"*, and in each word *the question mark represents a different letter of the alphabet.* Cross out the letters as you use them.

A   B   C   D   E   F   G   H   I   K   L   M
N   O   P   Q   R   S   T   U   V   W   X   Y   Z

1. D E I I O R S V ? _____

2. A D D E F N N T ? _____

3. A C D E I L P U ? _____

4. D D E I L N N O ? _____

5. C D I M R S T U ? _____

6. A C C D E E E N ? _____

7. A D I I I R S U ? _____

8. D D F I O O R T ? _____

9. C D F F I I T U ? _____

10. D D E E I O O R ? _____

11. A A D E I L L N ? _____

12. D D E F I I N T ? _____

13. A A D D E R S Y ? _____

14. A C C D E M O Y ? _____

15. D E G I I I L R ? _____

16. D I M O O R R T? _____

17. A C D I N O T T? _____

18. A D E N P R T V? _____

19. A A D E E T T V? _____

20. D E E I R T T Y? _____

21. C D E E E I T T? _____

22. B B D E L L M S? _____

23. D E L L O O S U? _____

24. A C D I L M O Y? _____

25. D E E I N R R R? _____

Compounding the Difficulty

Each set of letters for 1 through 13 contains two compound words. To compound the difficulty, sets 14 and 15 each contain four. See how many you can find.

Example: A D K L O O R W   <u>W O O D L A R K</u>
                               <u>W O R K L O A D</u>

1. A A E G T W Y   _____   _____

2. A B E E L N O P   _____   _____

3. A D M N O R S S W   _____   _____

4. D O O O P R S T   _____   _____

5. A E G H N O R V   _____   _____

6. E E K N O S T Y   _____   _____

7. E H O O P S T U   _____   _____

8. B F H I L O S W   _____   _____

9. A E E G L R S S   _____   _____

10. A B E G M N O Y   _____   _____

11. A B C D E I K S   _____   _____

12. A D E E S S W   _____   _____

13. D N N O R T U W   _____   _____

14. A E K O S T T U   _____   _____
                             _____   _____

15. A E E L M N S S   _____   _____
                             _____   _____

IMAGINATIVE INGMAR

Ingmar loves to try to stump his friends, the Brooklyn Scrabblettes, by giving them sets of letters which at first glance look unlikely to contain a word. Push your imagination to its outer limits, and see if you can meet Ingmar's challenge. You must use all the given letters and the question marks can represent any letter. Many are common words.

Example: F F F F ? ? ? ?   <u>R I F F R A F F</u>

1. D D D D ? ? ? ?   _ _ _ _ _ _ _ _

2. K K K ? ? ? ? ?   _ _ _ _ _ _ _ _

3. N N N N ? ? ? ?   _ _ _ _ _ _ _ _

4. R R R R ? ? ? ?   _ _ _ _ _ _ _ _

5. S S S S S ? ? ?   _ _ _ _ _ _ _ _

6. T T T T ? ? ? ?   _ _ _ _ _ _ _ _

7. U U U U ? ?   _ _ _ _ _ _

8. W W W ? ? ?   _ _ _ _ _ _
   _ _ _ _ _ _

9. A E I O U ? ?   _ _ _ _ _ _ _
   _ _ _ _ _ _ _

STUTTERING STANLEY

Stanley had weekly anagram lunches with his buddies, the Sherman clan, during which participants shouted out a word and a letter, and others tried to re-anagram them to find a new word. Because he stuttered, Stanley developed an interesting variation of this game. He called out two, three, or even four letters at a time.

Solve Stanley's anagram quizzes. Add one set of letters to a word below and anagram it to find a new word. Each set of letters will only go with one word to find another common word!

Example: O U T S W A M + H H
= M O U T H W A S H

E E E	G G	H H	I I I	M M M	N N N
O O O O	T T T	U U U	W W	Y Y	Z Z

1. MAESTRO _____

2. GIRLIES _____

3. ADIEU _____

4. SOONER _____

5. LEFTS _____

6. STABLE _____

7. IMPACT _____

8. STAND _____

9. STIPEND _____

10. COUSIN _____

11. STOMPS _____

STUTTERING STANLEY II

Stanley had weekly anagram lunches with his buddies during which participants shouted out a word and a letter, and others tried to re-anagram them to find a new word. Because he stuttered, Stanley developed an interesting variation of this game.

Solve Stanley's anagram quizzes. These are real "toughies," so we've given you the letters that go with each word to form another common word.

Example: O U T S W A M + H H
          = M O U T H W A S H

1. P L A N E T S + G G _____

2. P E E V E S + R R R _____

3. S A R D I N E + P P _____

4. D E N S E L Y + W W _____

5. M O U S E R + T T T _____

6. T A C K I E R + B B _____

7. S T U M P I E R + C C C _____

8. S T A M M E R + Y Y _____

9. P U S H E R + O O O _____

10. I N S I D E S + V V _____

11. T R A S H E S + U U _____

ANACRYPTICS

Undercover Agent

Grace Tenets, whose name anagrams to SECRET AGENT, is head of the F.I.B. An avid wordsmith, she secretly tracks her agents and their specialties and quirks by creating amusing anagrams. For example, AGENT SOUL, whose name anagrams to LANGOUSTE, loves seafood. Determine the anagram of the name Grace gives each agent from these clues.

1. AGENT DEE is very young.

2. AGENT VI always knows the year or place the dinner wine was produced.

3. AGENT YIP specializes in Middle Eastern affairs.

4. AGENT MIC has very attractive abilities.

5. AGENT SUT is extremely thin and bony.

6. AGENT PON is knowledgeable about the military.

7. AGENT KIL reminds Grace of a pesky bug.

8. AGENT LUM has a strange gray complexion, resembling his weapon.

9. AGENT DOWS and AGENT RAID are very theatrical.

10. AGENT FINT snacks a lot on chips and shakes.

11. AGENT ROUE is always surrounded by associates.

12. AGENT HUIR is more mischievous than the other agents.

13. AGENT ILYI is most pleasant and friendly.

14. AGENT PROD has a Mafia connection.

DEAR ONE

EVE SUFFI, whose name anagrams to EFFUSIVE, is just that, excessively demonstrative, often obnoxiously so. She hides a critical streak, however, that's anagrammed in her DEARs. For example, she greets a pompous and pretentious neighbor as DEAR CHUK, which anagrams to ARCHDUKE. Anagram Eve's greetings below to discover what she's really saying.

1. DEAR STYEY lives in the past.

2. DEAR UNDIP thinks her paycheck is too small.

3. DEAR AMI likes a little wine in the afternoon.

4. DEAR BINEL always talks about the Great Depression.

5. DEAR BROW never wears the same thing twice.

6. DEAR PORT just repeats what others say.

7. DEAR WREN has a rambling conversational style.

8. DEAR VITES loves to watch commercials.

9. DEAR GIES is very contentious.

10. DEAR FUDED once served time for swindling.

11. DEAR BECAF is an out-and-out liar.

12. DEAR BOBEL insisted on stating the obvious, over and over.

13. DEAR MOOSY is not one to look on the bright side.

14. DEAR HOSE loves to pick fights.

GIRL GUIDE

My Uncle Bari is definitely not with the feminist program. UNCLE BARI anagrams to INCURABLE. He calls all females "girls" and anagrams their names to conceal his true evaluation of their personality, appearance, or idiosyncrasies. For example, BIDIE GIRL, whose name anagrams to DIRIGIBLE, is slightly overweight and SAC GIRL, whose name anagrams to GARLICS, loves to cook pungent dishes. From the following clues, determine the hidden message in Bari's GIRLS.

1. PIM GIRL loves Thanksgiving.

2. RENE GIRL never goes home.

3. DAN GIRL is his favorite.

4. SALEE GIRL sneezes a lot.

5. FOME GIRL loves the movies.

6. MADA GIRL loves medieval lyric poetry.

7. HANO GIRL is interested in classical music.

8. PUFE GIRL often gets tickets for parking in illegal places.

9. SPUN GIRL is a noisy drinker.

10. DOCK GIRL often causes traffic jams.

11. BUTTE GIRL is very sloppy.

12. YADOO GIRL can see right through you.

13. BLUN GIRL loves Spanish sports and diversions.

14. ATOLA GIRL has very rough skin.

Hi There!

Bess Limed, whose name anagrams to DISSEMBLE, is very aware that her friends display the usual assortment of human faults, but slyly disguises her awareness with anagrams as she greets them. For example, she greets a friend who eats lots of cookies, "HELLO OUTS," an anagram for TOLLHOUSE. Uncover her appraisals.

1. HI BEMOAN greets a very unconventional friend.

2. She addresses a friend who is a little nuts with HI WEARY!

3. HI DOWSES! greets a friend who used to be in a circus.

4. Her tax lawyer receives a hearty HELLO POO.

5. She calls out HELLO OUDS to a friend who won't let anyone forget she once had the lead in an Ibsen play.

6. She says HELLO LEH to a neighbor with a miserable apartment.

7. HELLO AWES greets the best shopper on the block.

8. HELLO LIM salutes a gal who makes much of small slights.

9. HI MARCAR is her welcome for the block couch potato.

10. HI EVADES hails a person who gets into sticky situations.

YES-MAN

Everyone thought that Inver T. Ebrate was a yes-man. Much to his surprise, a fellow office wordsmith discovered that Inver used an anagram trick to secretly insult everyone in sight. For example, Inver said YES HEAD, which anagrams to HAYSEED, to the office yokel, and YES LAJOU, which anagrams to JEALOUSY, to someone who was green with envy. Anagram Inver's yes's below to discover his camouflaged ridicule.

1. He calls out YES BLAZON to the office sloth.

2. The teller of long, wandering stories is greeted with YES SODY.

3. He says YES ABLAW or YES CHANTI to the indecisive ones.

4. YES DAXIL is his welcome to people who can't get their letters straight.

5. He respectfully nods YES ARDENT to the immovable ones.

6. He heads memos to foul-mouthed Phil, YES BLAMPH.

7. He fawns YES LEFTER to the woman who does her own thing.

8. He commiserates YES LOURD to the guy who always expects a promotion.

9. He agrees, YES NABO, when Adele touts the healthy lunch.

10. He started saying YES NURGE to the boss when he gained weight.

SPELL CHECK

Sam Subtile, whose name anagrams to SUBLIMATES, is a great typist with a psychological tic which always gets him fired. When upset by someone, he deletes the letters of that person's name from words he is typing.

For example, when he was working for a bank and was mad at BOB, he produced this notice: "The point has been ELARED. I do not wish to be MASTIC, but customers must show their ANKOKS." The underlined letters should have been the words BELABORED, BOMBASTIC, and BANKBOOKS. Sam was fired again!

Determine in these sentences the subject of Sam's snit, and what the underlined words should have been. The place of employment is an extra clue.

1. *MEDICAL OFFICE:* This case is a perfect EPLE of the syndrome, probably resulting from a rare case of childhood SLLPO. Prescribed IBLE antibiotic to control PROYSS. To be REEINED in two weeks.

2. *FLORIST:* The latest shipment of ALLIS, as well as the SCOE trees, were received on May 15th. Expect ONET recompensation soon. When can we expect EPENT for those bad EADDE bows?

3. *AIR FORCE:* This memo is not to be construed as ANWOAN. However, it has come to our attention that COSEC residues have been found on UNIONS as well as on BOBSGHS. If this were WARE, the penalty would be extreme. Even in PEACEE, we must be vigilant!

4. *LAWYER:* I ask you not to FRUDGE. This man could be a OBHLDR or he could be a YRIDR. Before we are ADURND, I want to be assured that

you have not <u>PRCTED</u> your own guilt on him.

5. *COLLEGE RECRUITER:* Does your student want to be a <u>TRAPI</u>, or a <u>YGINI</u>? We are here to help with all the details, from <u>ALTIC</u> to <u>BDEES</u>. We are the finest educational institution in the <u>NORWT</u>.

6. *MISS LONELYHEARTS:* Dear <u>NONOUS</u>, do all in your power to settle this dispute <u>ICABL</u>. Your woes are not "<u>TEPORR</u>," do not <u>DDREA</u> that you will ever be more than a <u>PLATE</u>. Even if do receive <u>PLION</u> you can't warm your tootsies with money.

7. *COLUMNIST:* This was a year for odd trends; the most popular names for children born this year were <u>ASNE</u> and <u>BENAN</u>. Most popular wearing apparel: the <u>UPSUT</u>. Suddenly no one was using <u>ARUANA</u>, and the moral <u>AORTY</u> was in. And what happened to the English <u>AESTES</u>!

8. *TRAVEL WRITER:* This was not a <u>HCKEYE</u> experience! <u>LUCHE</u> into the <u>HEWIDS</u> at dawn, we <u>BLLOOE</u> a long <u>ISTCE</u> and felt as if we were going back to Kansas! The fact that it was just a little <u>GEROUS</u> added to the pleasure.

9. *TV NEWS:* And now a word from our <u>CHORMA</u>. The <u>SESTIOAL</u> story of the evening concerns the <u>ISURCE</u> <u>KIDPPIG</u> of A. M. Missing. There is <u>BUDAT</u> sentiment developing for the return of public <u>HGIGS</u>, should the criminals be found.

10. *MOVIE REVIEWER:* I think the <u>ARTNG</u> department got hold of this production by one of America's greatest <u>AVRC</u> <u>FLMARS</u> and really <u>GIMCD</u> it up. What could have been <u>DRALE</u> is only nightmarish.

LETTER PATTERNS

CIRCULAR VISION

In the letter circles below are six-letter words or ten-letter words with the letters in the correct order. You must, however, determine where each word begins and which direction around the circle the word reads. Doesn't that sound easy? See how quickly you can decipher them.

1.
```
   T   O
U         P
   A   I
```

2.
```
   S   U
E         A
   A   N
```

3.
```
   S   N
H         Y
   P   M
```

4.
```
   L   A
I         K
   A   L
```

5.
```
   A   I
L         R
   A   E
```

6.
```
   T   E
A         A
   I   V
```

7.
```
   A   N
M         Y
   O   D
```

8.
```
   K   N
E         I
   D   O
```

9.
```
   C   A
S         P
   E   E
```

10.
```
   D   E
E         I
   N   V
```

11. A D I
R   C
E   A
D E T

12. E F R
R   E
E   T
R I N

13. N U M
E   E
R   R
A T E

14. N D U
A   M
R   M
O M E

15. A L Y
C   P
U   T
E S U

16. N D O
E   S
C   C
S E R

17. S O P
T   A
R   E
O P H

18. E N O
L   R
L   T
A C I

19. S E Y
T   R
E   A
R Y E

20. N A T
E   E
V   R
U J E

CIRCULAR VISION II

Circle the globe in search of famous people, past and present. The letter circles below contain eight letters and blanks in correct order. Figure out where the name, usually a surname, begins and which direction to read. To challenge you, we've omitted many letters but provided hints.

Hints (not in order): Iranian religious leader * First Roman emperor * American actor, voice of Charlie * French marine explorer * Nine popes had this name * West German chancellor * American follies (1907–1931) producer * Italian violinist

1. — S
    — Y
    — T
    — —

2. — —
    N
    I   —
    F —   —

3. — —
    E   —
    U A —

4. — U
    U   U
    — —

5. — U
    E   —
    — —
    S —

6. H —
    — —
    — —
    N I

7. — I
    — —
    — A G —

8. — G
    — —
    — E
    — L

50

CIRCULAR VISION III

Circle the globe in search of famous people, past and present. The letter circles below contain eight letters and blanks in correct order. Figure out where the name, usually a surname, begins and which direction to read. To challenge you, we've omitted many letters but provided hints.

Hints (not in order): Inventor and manufacturer of safety razor * Russian dancer * English poet laureate * Italian explorer * British prime minister * *The Blue Angel* * *Saturday Evening Post* illustrator * Singer of "You're No Good"

1.
```
    __  N
  __      N
  N
        __
    __  __
```

5.
```
       __  I
   I        __
   __        S
       __  __
```

2.
```
     I  __
   __      __
   __      S
     __  P
```

6.
```
     I  L
   __      __
   __    __
     __  T
```

3.
```
     __  __
   __      __
   __      T
     H  A
```

7.
```
       __  K
   __        W
   __        E
       __  __
```

4.
```
     __  A
   __      D
   __      T
     __  __
```

8.
```
     C  H
   __      __
   __    __
     __  E
```

CIRCULAR VISION IV

Circle the globe in search of famous people, past and present. The letter circles below contain eight letters and blanks in correct order. Figure out where the name, usually a surname, begins and which direction to read. To challenge you, we've omitted many letters but provided hints.

Hints (not in order): *The Second Sex* author * Soviet president (1960–1964) * American anchorman * Spanish singer and heartthrob * Greek philosopher-cynic * American industrialist and philanthropist * Austrian composer (1797–1828) * LBJ's VP

1.
```
    __  G
__       E
__       N
   __ __
```

2.
```
    __ __ R
__        O
__     N
   __  N
```

3.
```
    __ __ U
__        A
__     E
   __ E
```

4.
```
   R  E
__       __
__       H
   __ __
```

5.
```
    __  I
__       __
__       L
   S  __
```

6.
```
    C  H
__       __
T        __
   __ __
```

7.
```
    __  M
__       P
__       __
   E  __
```

8.
```
    G  I
__       E
__       __
   __ __
```

SWITCHEROO

Keeping the given letter sequence, change the position of *only one* letter in each word below to make a new word.

Example: STARTLES, STARLETS

1. EMPATHIC *Pathetic*
2. LAMBKINS
3. CLACKING
4. LUMBERS
5. STOPPING
6. SLINGING
7. RUSTIEST
8. SLOWDOWN
9. TASTELESS
10. DISCREETLY
11. DOORLESS
12. AMENABLE
13. USABILITY
14. OVERDOES
15. PRETENSE

16. COMPLAINT
17. BLANKEST
18. CRUSTILY
19. LATITUDE
20. STRIDENT
21. COMPARED
22. OCTILLION
23. SINISTER
24. IMMERSED
25. EGOCENTRIC
26. CAUSALLY
27. OVERBUYS
28. ARMORIES
29. FASTBACK
30. THATCHES

Switcheroo II

Keeping the given letter sequence, change the position of *only one* letter in each word below to make a new word.

Example: REPLATE, PRELATE

1. CHARING
2. MINUTE
3. PREMISE
4. UGLIEST
5. EVENER
6. EMANATE
7. ENERVATE
8. UNROOFS
9. BRASIERS
10. REPETEND
11. PRIMEROS
12. REFIGHTS
13. PALMISTS
14. TARRIERS
15. ANCHOR
16. EPIGON
17. LINKING
18. HOWEVER
19. DEIFIED
20. CUTTLE
21. HEARTIER
22. WRENCHES
23. PYROGEN
24. LEARIEST
25. EVILNESS
26. TRUMPETS
27. TICKLER
28. PILLAGES
29. HARICOT
30. DISSERVE

WORD PATTERNS

MIDDLEMAN

Insert one letter set from column A in the space provided in column B to form a seven-, eight-, or nine-letter word. Each set in column A can only be used once.

Example: P E <u>D A L</u> E D

Column A

A R B

A V O

B I Z

E L L

E T H

G I B

H I N

I L L

K E A

M A C

M O G

N O O

T E W

T U I

T Y E

U L U

X I S

Column B

1. F O R E _ _ _ N

2. R O U _ _ _ A Y

3. S P _ _ _ X E S

4. H O _ _ _ E N Y

5. G R I _ _ _ E D

6. L I _ _ _ B L E

7. T A N _ _ _ L E

8. G R A _ _ _ T Y

9. O U _ _ _ L L

10. F L _ _ _ R

11. U R _ _ _ R A

12. G E _ _ _ O X

13. A R A _ _ _ E D

14. P A B _ _ _ M S

15. D U _ _ _ E R

16. S E _ _ _ M S

17. S P _ _ _ W A Y

MIDDLEMAN II

Insert one letter set from column A in the space provided in column B to form a seven-, eight-, or nine-letter word. Each set in column A can only be used once.

Example: S O <u>M E D</u> A Y

Column A	Column B
C E P	1. A R T __ __ __ O K E
C I S	2. B A __ __ __ K A
C O R	3. D E __ __ __ U M
E T H	4. B O __ __ __ O N
G A N	5. M O __ __ __ R A M
G E Y	6. A N __ __ __ O P E
I C H	7. I N __ __ __ O R
K E F	8. B O __ __ __ M A N
L I N	9. O R E __ __ __ O S
M O L	10. B I O __ __ __ E S
N O G	11. S A U __ __ __ A N
P S I	12. T E L __ __ __ O N
T E L	13. T O __ __ __ A Y
U R B	14. W A __ __ __ U L
U T A	15. J E T __ __ __ E R
W A W	16. A M P __ __ __ T E D
Z O O	17. U N __ __ __ T E N

57

CLOAK AND DAGGER

How clever of the F.B.I. to hide in the middle of SURFBIRD! The C.I.A., similarly secretive, lies in wait to complete one of the letter sets in column B. Insert one common American abbreviation from column A in the space provided in column B to form a new word. Each abbreviation in column A can only be used once.

Extra Credit: What does each abbreviation represent?

Example: S U R <u>F B I</u> R D

Column A		Column B
A T M	1.	V I C T _ _ _ _ O D
C A R E	2.	B E V _ _ _ G E
C I A	3.	E F _ _ _ _ _ C Y
D D S	4.	A _ _ _ _ _ M I E S
E R A	5.	D O W _ _ _ N G E
F I C A	6.	B E A _ _ _ _ G
G O P	7.	C _ _ _ _ _ H E T Y
N A S A	8.	S _ _ _ _ _ C R O W
N A T O	9.	E N _ _ _ _ _ H E
N B A	10.	_ _ _ _ _ L L Y
N R A	11.	S E _ _ _ _ A T E
I M H O	12.	O L I _ _ _ O L Y
P T A	13.	S P E _ _ _ L
R O T C	14.	S H O _ _ _ L K
S W A T	15.	O _ _ _ _ M A K E R

CLOAK AND DAGGER II

How clever of the F.B.I. to hide in the middle of SURF-BIRD! Insert one common American abbreviation from column A in the space provided in column B to form a new word. Each abbreviation in column A can only be used once.

Extra Credit: What does each abbreviation represent?

Example: S U R <u>F B</u> I R D

Column A	**Column B**
C O D	1. P O __ __ O R N
D A R	2. G U __ __ __ I N T
F Y I	3. Z __ __ __ Y
M D	4. O __ __ __ I O N
N F L	5. A __ __ __ T I C
N O W	6. P O S T __ __ __ E
E S T	7. G __ __ __ D
P C	8. C H O __ __ __ U N D
P I N	9. G E N __ __ __ M E
P L O	10. H U __ __ R U M
S E P	11. N O __ __ __ N E R
U A R	12. U N I __ __ __ N G
U P I	13. M A __ __ __ L E U M
W H O	14. H A __ __ __ I D
U S O	15. M A R S __ __ __ A L

NOT VERY EASY PUZZLE

Keep the order given in the letter strings below. Add the letters from the word E A S Y, not necessarily in order, to uncover some common words which may not be easy to find.

Example: __ T R __ T __ G __   <u>S</u> T R <u>A</u> T <u>E</u> G <u>Y</u>

1. P __ R __ L __ __

2. __ M B __ S __ __

3. N O __ __ G __ __

4. W __ __ __ I D __

5. __ __ S __ M B L __

6. __ P R __ __ __ R

7. R O __ __ M __ R __

8. G R __ __ N __ __ S

9. __ __ M I N __ R __

10. O V __ R __ T __ __

11. M __ __ T __ R __

12. L O __ __ L T I __ __

13. J __ __ L O U __ __

14. __ M __ T H __ __ T

15. __ __ __ __ __ T I E R

16. __ N C __ __ T R __

17. __ __ E __ T R __ I N

18. __ __ N D I C __ T __

19. T __ P __ C __ __ T

20. __ C C __ __ S O R __

21. H O R __ __ P L __ __

22. __ E __ T __ R D __ Y

23. P __ __ S __ R B __

24. __ __ L __ S L A D __

60

QUITE A HARD PUZZLE

Keep the order given in the letter strings below; add the letters from the word H A R D (not necessarily in order) to uncover some common words which are quite hard to find.

Example: W I T __ __ __ __ W   W I T H D R A W

1. __ __ __ I S __
2. O R C __ __ __ __
3. __ __ Y __ I __ E
4. __ __ I __ __ O
5. V E __ __ N __ A __
6. __ E __ __ E __ D
7. P __ I L __ N __ E __
8. C __ E D __ __ __ S
9. __ U T __ O __ E __
10. __ __ U G __ T E __
11. __ I S __ W __ __ E
12. __ I S C __ __ __ G E
13. B I __ T __ __ __ Y
14. U N __ E __ __ __ __
15. F __ T __ E __ E __
16. S __ I P Y __ __ __
17. F O O L __ __ __ __ Y
18. A __ R O W __ E __ __
19. __ Y __ __ __ U L I C
20. C A __ __ S __ __ R P
21. __ E __ Y D __ __ T E
22. W __ T E __ S __ E __
23. U N __ E __ __ __ __ N D
24. D __ S __ B O A __ __

REALLY TOUGH PUZZLE

Keep the order given in the letter strings below. Add the letters from the word T O U G H, not necessarily in order, to uncover some common words which are really tough to find.

Example: S _ _ _ _ I N _   S H O U T I N G

1. D R _ _ _ _ _

2. S _ A _ _ _ _ N D

3. S _ _ _ _ _ N S

4. _ A N _ _ _ _

5. _ _ _ _ _ I E

6. Y _ _ _ _ R _

7. A _ _ _ _ R A P _

8. _ _ T _ R O W _ _

9. A L _ H _ _ _ _

10. _ R _ _ C _ I E S _

11. _ _ _ S E _ U E S _

12. _ V E R B O _ _ _ _

13. B I _ M _ _ _ _

14. _ _ _ R I _ _ T

15. D _ _ _ _ N U _

16. R _ _ _ _ E S _

17. _ H O R _ _ _ _

TRIVIA AND WORD MEANINGS

THESPIANS

Acting on your instincts, find the words ending in
-IAN(S) below. We've given you brief hints.

Example: Beetle Bailey wasn't one. C I V I L I A N

1. Most politicians aren't these. _ _ _ _ _ I A N S

2. Eddie's father [*The Munsters*] worked for one.
   _ _ _ _ _ _ I A N

3. In *The Music Man,* Marian was one.
   _ _ _ _ _ _ I A N

4. Up to monkey business? _ _ _ I A N

5. Born under the 11th sign of the Zodiac.
   _ _ _ _ _ I A N

6. It's prime. _ _ _ _ _ I A N

7. Kermit is one. _ _ _ _ _ _ _ I A N

8. Cold-blooded and frequently scaly-skinned.
   _ _ _ _ _ _ I A N

9. Four-legged, may ride red trucks.
   _ _ _ _ _ _ I A N

10. Person of high birth, aristocrat.
    _ _ _ _ _ _ I A N

11. Some "Beverly Hills 90210" grads become these.
    _ _ _ _ _ _ I A N S

12. Some Shakespearean actors.
    _ _ _ _ _ _ I A N S

Colorful Speech

Below are definitions of words or phrases that begin with the name of a color. For example, a person who brings his lunch in a sack is a "brown bagger." See how many you can find.

1. Gardening pro _____

2. To cover or gloss over _____

3. Policeman's sick-out _____

4. Area of prostitution _____

5. Nazi storm trooper _____

6. Commercial section of phone book

   _____

7. Attack as a Communist _____

8. One who comes to the rescue _____

9. A wife-slayer, from folktale _____

10. Inexperienced person _____

11. Karate expert _____

12. "Do unto others . . ." _____

13. Syracuse University athletes _____

14. Overly complex procedures _____

15. Motion pictures _____

16. Drinker's hallucinations _____

17. Sought by Jason and the Argonauts

   _____

18. Optimistic eyes _____

Colorful Speech II

Below are definitions of words or phrases that begin with the name of a color. For example, to ingratiate or curry favor is to brownnose. See how many you can find.

1. Business loss _____

2. Magical weapon to solve long-standing problem
   _____

3. Charmer out for gifts and money
   _____

4. Cocktail using grenadine _____

5. Work shirker _____

6. Brains, intelligence _____

7. Card game or a weapon _____

8. Anti-union agreement _____

9. Middle-class blandness _____

10. Vigorous, lusty _____

11. Intense gravitational field in space
    _____

12. Poetic for jealousy _____

13. A type of rummage sale _____

14. Discredited family member _____

15. Sensational news coverage _____

16. Extortion by threat of exposure
    _____

LANGUAGE SHAPE-UP

Below are definitions of words or phrases that contain the name of a shape or geometric figure. For example, a dance involving four couples and a caller is a SQUARE DANCE. See how many you can find.

1. Texas state nickname _____

2. Where the President works _____

3. Feeling or impression of romance, magic, or ethereality _____

4. A tournament in which every contestant is matched against every other contestant

   _____

5. Starting point; one sometimes goes back there!

   _____

6. Popular place to welcome the New Year

   _____

7. Most accident-prone spot in the Atlantic?

   _____

8. Selling scam _____

9. These can't be avoided when driving in Washington, D.C. _____

10. Member of Parliamentary party in England during Puritan times _____

11. A just and honest person _____

12. He, she, and she, sometimes _____

13. It guided the Magi _____

14. Garage for locomotives? _____

15. Quilting group _____

TRANSFORMERS

Practice your word alchemy. Use the definition given to determine the short word. Then extend that word to make another word which fits the second definition.

Example: Very young child ⟶ foot soldiers
INFANT ⟶ INFANTRY

1. Hidden, undercover ⟶ writing desk

   — — — — — —   — — — — — — — — —

2. Vaulting equipment ⟶ aggressive refutation

   — — — —   — — — — — — —

3. Curved structural support ⟶ study of artifacts

   — — — —   — — — — — — — — — —

4. Hair-care device ⟶ fighter

   — — — —   — — — — — — — —

5. Type of word play ⟶ to pierce

   — — —   — — — — — — —

6. German composer ⟶ unattached male

   — — — —   — — — — — — — —

7. Men's party ⟶ scenery worker

   — — — —   — — — — — — — — —

8. Strap to control animal ⟶ fresh embodiment

   — — — —   — — — — — — — — — — — — —

9. Domestic canine ⟶ casual verse

   — — —   — — — — — — — —

10. To carry ⟶ without facial hair

   — — — —   — — — — — — — —

TRANSFORMERS II

Practice your word alchemy. Use the definition given to determine the short word. Then extend that word to make another word which fits the second definition.

Example: Candid and open ⟶ Wise Men's gift
FRANK ⟶ FRANKINCENSE

1. Decipher written symbols ⟶ regulate again

___ ___ ___ ___ ___ ___ ___ ___ ___ ___ ___ ___

2. Orderly procedure ⟶ agricultural estate

___ ___ ___ ___ ___ ___ ___ ___ ___ ___ ___ ___ ___

3. Type of gambling machine ⟶ lazy

___ ___ ___ ___ ___ ___ ___ ___ ___ ___ ___

4. Hollow sounding device ⟶ whine and complain

___ ___ ___ ___ ___ ___ ___ ___ ___ ___

5. Short for father ⟶ aggressive photographer

___ ___ ___ ___ ___ ___ ___ ___ ___ ___ ___ ___ ___

6. Type of club ⟶ unease

___ ___ ___ ___ ___ ___ ___ ___ ___ ___ ___ ___ ___ ___

7. Type of currency ⟶ similar occurences

___ ___ ___ ___ ___ ___ ___ ___ ___ ___ ___ ___ ___

8. Plunge into water ⟶ compulsory transfer of stock

___ ___ ___ ___ ___ ___ ___ ___ ___ ___ ___ ___ ___ ___

9. One hired for group scene in movie ⟶ lavish

___ ___ ___ ___ ___ ___ ___ ___ ___ ___ ___ ___ ___ ___

10. Short for M.D. ⟶ factual film

___ ___ ___ ___ ___ ___ ___ ___ ___ ___ ___ ___

TRANSFORMERS III

Practice your word alchemy. Use the definition given to determine the short word. Then extend that word to make another word which fits the second definition.

Example: Moving vehicle ⟶ to conquer
VAN ⟶ VANQUISH

1. Body of students ⟶ type of ad

_ _ _ _ _   _ _ _ _ _ _ _ _ _ _ _

2. Dull a light ⟶ measurement

_ _ _   _ _ _ _ _ _ _ _ _

3. Auto ⟶ exaggerated depiction

_ _ _   _ _ _ _ _ _ _ _ _

4. Animal lair ⟶ inhabitant

_ _ _   _ _ _ _ _ _ _

5. To author ⟶ jail

_ _ _   _ _ _ _ _ _ _ _ _ _ _

6. French father ⟶ long-lived plant

_ _ _ _   _ _ _ _ _ _ _ _ _

7. Type of rodent ⟶ defense mechanism

_ _ _   _ _ _ _ _ _ _ _ _ _ _ _

8. Type of boat ⟶ deception

_ _ _   _ _ _ _ _ _ _ _ _

9. To engage in a winter sport ⟶ minor fight

_ _ _   _ _ _ _ _ _ _

10. Golf standard ⟶ punctuation marks

_ _ _   _ _ _ _ _ _ _ _ _ _

LARRY AND
DIANE'S DIVERSIONS

DIANE'S DECEPTIVE DIARY

Diane thought she could conceal the identities of her friends in her diary by using anagrams of their names. For example, she used the word EVENTS, which is an anagram of the name Steven. Below are the words her snoopy sister cleverly found and deciphered. Can you? By the way, some of Diane's friends have foreign or unusual names.

1. riding
2. dryable
3. corrida
4. Armenian
5. allure
6. virgin
7. snidely
8. bather
9. Crimean
10. yawned
11. uraemic
12. redone
13. hamlet
14. angled
15. yonder

16. habitat
17. aimless
18. oilcans
19. cerulean
20. heaters
21. palaces
22. inclosure
23. toaster
24. dragline
25. saloon
26. realigned
27. ordinals
28. sailable
29. threes (2 names)
30. lardon (3 names)

Super Snoop Credit: In the letters given, find two eight-letter names which are anagrams of each other:
A D E H O O R T.

LITERAL LARRY'S TRAVELOG

Literal Larry decided to make some travelogs using his new video camera. He was certain, however, that he could only shoot places whose names contained the letters in the word LOG, not necessarily in order. For example, his first work featured the lovely city of COraL Gables, Florida. From the descriptions below, determine the other places he filmed.

1. The former capital of Nigeria, a port city   Lagos

2. French city famous for manufacture of fine porcelain of same name   Limoge

3. Its breakaway republics provoked United Nations peacekeeping action   yugoslavia

4. Gatsby lived here; also expressway called "the world's longest parking lot"   Long island freeway

5. River which joins the Allegheny River to form the Ohio River   Monongahela

6. Joan Didion's turf, West Coast megalopolis   Los Angelos

7. Asian region which includes the Gobi Desert; also, with Outer, a republic   Mongolia

8. Former colonial giant, situated in western Iberian peninsula   Portugal

9. Biblical Calvary's Hebrew name

10. Ecuadorean islands visited by Darwin and the *Beagle*   galapagos

11. Industrial city and port in Scotland   Glasgow

12. Russian river flowing into the Caspian Sea; also "boat song"   Volga

13. Strait connecting San Francisco Bay with Pacific Ocean

14. Site of United States Air Force Academy   Colorado springs

Literal Larry's Two-Timers

Larry heard the expression "two-timers" and riddled it this way: a *two-timer* has a deep-seated attraction to double syllables. Therefore, a two-timer would go gaga about traveling to Bora Bora or Walla-Walla with Zsa Zsa. Use the clues below to determine other two-timing preferences.

1. A North African steamed grain specialty
2. Two wardrobe items: loose Hawaiian garment; Polynesian skirt Mao Mao
3. Two kinds of ammunition
4. Cheerleader's equipment pom-pons
5. Popular fish entree, and accompanying sauce Mahi Mah
6. Fly responsible for transmitting sleeping sickness Tse Tse
7. Disease caused by thiamine deficiency
8. Two energetic dances Go-Go,
9. A relish or a dog Chow-Chow
10. Spear-throwing device
11. Twin terms for frilly or showy ornamentation
12. Fetish, charm, magic
13. Extinct flightless bird Do Do
14. Tree with edible fruit, custard apple family
15. Hawaiian goose
16. Pedal mute for electric guitar
17. Kind of drum

LITERAL LARRY'S CROSSWORDS

Larry's literal and very punny version of a crossword puzzle requires that you find two words which share the given middle letter. To help you solve the puzzles, he has also given you the first letters of the words.

1. Egyptian girlie magazine?

P
—
P _ _ Y _ _ _
—
—
—

2. Glacial Rorschach?

I
—
I _ _ B _ _ _ _
—
—
—

3. Power Ranger's facial?

M
—
M _ _ P _ _ _
—
—
—

4. Lestat's commute?

V
—
V _ _ P _ _ _
—
—
—

5. Weatherman's joke?

W
—
—
W _ _ _ C _ _ _ _
—
—
—
—

6. Notre Damer's car?

H
—
—
H _ _ _ H _ _ _ _
—
—
—

LITERAL LARRY'S CROSSWORDS II

1. Tavern girl's radio?

<pre>
          B
          _
     B _ _ M _ _ _ _
          _
          _
          _
</pre>

2. Green for an Irish lass?

<pre>
          C
          _
     C _ _ L _ _ _ _
          _
          _
</pre>

3. Venetian confection?

<pre>
          G
          _
     G _ _ D _ _ _
          _
          _
          _
</pre>

4. Riding pants for Archie friend?

<pre>
          J
          _
     J _ _ H _ _ _
          _
          _
          _
</pre>

5. Country singer protector?

<pre>
          B
          _
          _
     B _ _ _ G _ _ _ _
          _
          _
          _
          _
</pre>

6. Star Wars' Luke's toast spread?

<pre>
          S
          _
          _
     M _ _ _ A _ _ _ _
          _
          _
          _
</pre>

ANSWERS

Anagram and Hook Riddles

Anagrammatize

1. hikers shriek
2. risqué squire
3. porter report
4. despot depots
5. stout touts
6. green genre
7. mouse moues
8. found fondu
9. pasty patsy
10. cruel ulcer

Anagrammatize II

1. chapter patcher
2. testee settee
3. soupcon coupons
4. ribald bridal
5. soaring signora
6. process corpses
7. boosting bongoist
8. enamored demeanor
9. bundist dustbin
10. stubbier subtribe

Anagrammatize III

1. tramline terminal
2. cruiser curries
3. trimmed midterm
4. slimiest elitisms
5. mooniest emotions
6. cowherd chowder
7. bizarre brazier
8. brawler warbler
9. mantrap rampant
10. funfair ruffian

Anagrammatize IV

1. feigned feeding
2. trijet jitter
3. redolent rondelet
4. prosiest ripostes
5. deviates' sedative
6. nightcap patching
7. sleuth hustle
8. rustled strudel
9. dilatory idolatry
10. gestapo postage

Anagrammatize V

1. versatile relatives
2. continued unnoticed
3. mechanic's mischance
4. masculine calumnies
5. corselet selector
6. timesaving negativism
7. supersonic percussion
8. stipulated platitudes
9. raunchier hurricane
10. alignment lamenting

Anagrammatize VI

1. steamship shipmates
2. mountaineer enumeration
3. repossess espressos
4. peripatetic precipitate
5. conservation conversation
6. terrorise roisterer
7. halfback's flashback
8. persistent prettiness
9. striptease tapestries
10. optometric competitor

DOUBLE TAKE

1. holstein hot lines
2. rest home theorems
3. near-miss seminars
4. lost-cause cassoulet
5. diviner drive-in
6. cowhands' cash down
7. foretell toll free
8. cassette test case
9. chicken check-in
10. sea dogs' dosages
11. per diem impeder
12. laggard's glad rags
13. creakiest ice skater
14. banshee has-been
15. bearskin break-in
16. technocrat trench coat

HOOK SHOTS

1. PREDAWN SUNDIAL
   Equipped
   Islander
   Playoff
   Sunlit
   Uneaten
   Wageless
   Nemesis
   Dalliance
   Revert
   Alikeness
   Neither
   Dapple
   Atrophies
   Lionize

2. PARAPET
   Abasement
   Emergence
   Relapse
   Preserve
   Amounted
   Preview
   Thereafter

3. HOPSCOTCH
   Twinning
   Cravings
   Otitis
   Hairier
   Proof
   Odour
   Haloes
   Select
   Chiding

4. HOPPING MAD
   Ghost
   Nova
   Parson
   Mascot
   Aspire
   Ivied
   Plucky
   Hairbrush
   Driver
   Opinioned

5. FREEBOOTS
   Terror
   Factor
   Stiff
   Elicit
   Revery
   Orally
   Elapse
   Beagle
   Ozone

6. HELLCAT
   Crumple
   Harmless
   Languish
   Atheist
   Emigrant
   Literate
   Tweedier

7. POCKET WATCH
   Covert
   Kiwis
   Afloat
   Hairline
   Coldish
   Enumerate
   Tokay
   Oration
   Probing
   Thornlike
   Whelm

8. **BLACK BALL**
   Chaste   Limitable   Broadside
   Knave   Lapse   Avail
   Abroad   Lament   Bleak
9. **CRACKPOT**
   Crockery   Reviler   Carouse
   Asteroid   Phoney   Ocarina
   Tenfold   Kneed
10. **PAL JOEY**
   Orangy   Jargon   Loverly
   Abasement   Presume
   Yegg   Espouse

CATEGORY ANAGRAMS

COMMON SENSE

1. a. SCULPTOR
   b. PRINTMAKER
   c. CARTOONIST
   d. CERAMIST
   e. PAINTER
   Types of Artist

2. a. GAMES
   b. PEOPLE
   c. GLAMOUR
   d. GOURMET
   e. SEVENTEEN
   Popular Magazines

3. a. CATS
   b. HAIR
   c. HAMLET
   d. CAROUSEL
   e. ANTIGONE
   Plays

4. a. CANCER
   b. ARIES
   c. VIRGO
   d. AQUARIUS
   e. PISCES
   Signs of the Zodiac

5. a. LIFE
   b. CHEERIOS
   c. OATMEAL
   d. GRANOLA
   e. WHEATIES
   Breakfast Cereals

6. a. KEEPER
   b. CAGES
   c. ELEPHANT
   d. GIRAFFE
   e. LEOPARD
   Things at the Zoo

7. a. LIBERAL
   b. SOCIALIST
   c. COMMUNIST
   d. DEMOCRATIC
   e. REPUBLICAN
   Political Parties

8. a. CARMEL
   b. CONCORD
   c. CHICAGO
   d. CLEVELAND
   e. CHARLESTON
   U.S. Cities Beginning with "C"

Common Sense II

1. a. CHARLESTON
   b. MONKEY
   c. SQUARE
   d. POLKA
   e. CONGA
   Dances

2. a. (DIANE) SAWYER
   b. (DAN) RATHER
   c. (HARRY) REASONER
   d. (TOM) BROKAW
   e. (BARBARA) WALTERS
   Newscasters

3. a. SCREWDRIVER
   b. MANHATTAN
   c. MARTINI
   d. GIMLET
   e. ALEXANDER
   Mixed Drinks

4. a. FISH
   b. HEARTS
   c. BRIDGE
   d. PINOCHLE
   e. SOLITAIRE
   Card Games

5. a. BORSCHT
   b. BISQUE
   c. CONSOMMÉ
   d. BOUILLON
   e. PUREE
   Types of Soup

6. a. WISDOM
   b. INCISORS
   c. EYE
   d. FALSE
   e. BICUSPIDS
   Teeth

7. a. DOLPHINS
   b. COWBOYS
   c. PACKERS
   d. RAIDERS
   e. STEELERS
   Superbowl Winners

8. a. NEWPORT
   b. CAMEL
   c. WINSTON
   d. MARLBORO
   e. SALEM
   Brands of Cigarette

9. a. GUM
   b. HONEY
   c. SITUATIONS
   d. GLUE
   e. LOLLIPOP
   Sticky Things

10. a. MARCONI
    b. FRANKLIN
    c. EDISON
    d. FULTON
    e. WHITNEY
    Inventors

Common Sense III

1. a. CHARITY
   b. COTTON
   c. BEACH
   d. TENNIS
   e. RUBBER
   Balls

2. a. ENTERPRISE
   b. SPOCK
   c. CHEKOV
   d. SCOTTY
   e. KLINGONS
   Star Trek Things

3. a. MANDIBLE
   b. FIBULA
   c. RADIUS
   d. PATELLA
   e. HUMERUS
   Bones

4. a. SILVER
   b. TRIGGER
   c. LASSIE
   d. FLIPPER
   e. MORRIS
   Famous TV Animals

5. a. SAND
   b. LOAN
   c. HAMMERHEAD
   d. MAKO
   e. TIGER
   Sharks

6. a. HOUDINI
   b. MERLIN
   c. BLACKSTONE
   d. HENNING
   e. COPPERFIELD
   Magicians

7. a. POPCORN
   b. TEARS
   c. MARGARITA
   d. OCEAN
   e. PRETZELS
   Salty Things

8. a. RANSOM
   b. CHINATOWN
   c. CABARET
   d. SHAMPOO
   e. ALIEN
   One-Word Movie Titles

9. a. BALLROOM
   b. AEROBIC
   c. BALLET
   d. MODERN
   e. COUNTRY
   Types of Dancing

10. a. LAVENDER
    b. OREGANO
    c. ANGELICA
    d. CORIANDER
    e. TARRAGON
    Herbs

COMMON SENSE IV

1. a. RELECTOR
   b. LOBSTER
   b. SUNBURN
   d. CARDINAL
   e. LIGHTS
   Things That Are Red

2. a. AMETHYST
   b. DIAMOND
   c. TOPAZ
   d. SAPPHIRE
   e. EMERALD
   Birthstones

3. a. EARHART
   b. LINDBERGH
   c. WRIGHT
   d. ROGERS
   e. LOCKHEED
   Famous Aviators

4. a. WOODSTOCK
   b. GARFIELD
   c. DAGWOOD
   d. VERONICA
   e. CATHY
   Cartoon Characters

5. a. HAZEL
   b. MACADAMIA
   c. ALMOND
   d. PISTACHIO
   e. HICKORY
   Nuts

6. a. FRENCH
   b. ITALIAN
   c. MATZO
   d. PUMPERNICKEL
   e. WHITE
   Breads

7. a. LA GUARDIA
   b. DULLES
   c. HOBBY
   d. LOGAN
   e. KENNEDY
   Airports Named after People

8. a. MAGNUM
   b. IRONSIDE
   c. ROCKFORD
   d. COLUMBO
   e. TENNISON
   TV Detectives

9. a. ELECTRIC
   b. WHEEL
   c. FOLDING
   d. HIGH
   e. LOUNGE
   Types of Chair

10. a. PEPPER
    b. RUTH
    c. DOOLITTLE
    d. LIVINGSTON
    e. JEKYLL
    Doctors

COMMON SENSE V

1. a. KHRUSHCHEV
   b. STALIN
   c. LENIN
   d. BREZHNEV
   e. GORBACHEV
   Famous Russians

2. a. CARAT
   b. KILOGRAM
   c. PENNYWEIGHT
   d. POUND
   e. GRAIN
   Units of Weight

3. a. CARPENTER
   b. WHITE
   c. SHEPARD
   d. ALDRIN
   e. LOVELL
   U.S. Astronauts

4. a. HEROIN
   b. MARIJUANA
   c. HASHISH
   d. OPIUM
   e. MESCALINE
   Illegal Drugs

5. a. YANGTZE
   b. THAMES
   c. JORDAN
   d. AMAZON
   e. SEINE
   Rivers

6. a. MINIM
   b. DRAM
   c. PINT
   d. GALLON
   e. LITER
   Units of Capacity

7. a. TAXICAB
   b. LEMON
   c. COWARD
   d. CANARY
   e. BANANA
   Things That Are Yellow

8. a. NICOISE
   b. CAESAR
   c. WALDORF
   d. SPINACH
   e. COLESLAW
   Salads

9. a. GOOSE
   b. GATE
   c. OLDIE
   d. RULE
   e. GLOVES
   Things Golden

10. a. SUNTAN
    b. OLIVE
    c. MOTOR
    d. PEANUT
    e. SAFFLOWER
    Oils

Tough Anagrams and Beyond

Stretching Your Mind

1. borax, boxcar
2. capon, canopy
3. pouty, payout
4. visit, vibist
5. brick, bicker
6. ruder, murder
7. clock, cockle
8. pinup, upping
9. rhino, heroin
10. vigil, living
11. naval, vandal
12. sushi, squish
13. limit, mislit
14. sauté, salute
15. lymph, phylum
16. myrrh, rhymer

Stretching Your Mind II

1. retakes, streaked
2. glories, glossier
3. gathers, shortage
4. coasted, accosted
5. restore, reroutes
6. dollies, collides
7. transit, transmit
8. spoiler, profiles
9. tainted, attained
10. scorned, consider
11. basting, dingbats
12. dossier, soldiers
13. tarnish, trashing
14. readmit, mediator
15. dithers, thirsted
16. meanies, examines

Black and White

1. WITCHERY
2. OTHERWISE
3. SWEETISH
4. CHEWIEST
5. HEREWITH
6. DISHWATER
7. TWENTIETH
8. WHACKIEST
9. LENGTHWISE
10. PACKABLE
11. BACKSLIDE
12. ROADBLOCK
13. CLAMBAKES
14. BLACKBIRD
15. CAMELBACK
16. BLOCKADE
17. LOCKABLE

Anagram Annie

1. CLARINET + Y = CERTAINLY
2. PRIMATES + N = SPEARMINT
3. SPRAINED + P = SANDPIPER
4. RUMINATE + I = MINIATURE
5. BINARIES + T = BRAINIEST
6. VENETIAN + L = VALENTINE
7. BEATNIKS + E = SNAKEBITE
8. SEMINARY + H = HYMNARIES
9. MISTAKEN + O = ANTISMOKE
10. CRAZIEST + O = OSTRACIZE
11. DANDIEST + L = TIDELANDS
12. MEANTIME + C = MINCEMEAT
13. SCENARIO + X = ANOREXICS
14. VINEGARS + H = RESHAVING
15. VIBRATES + L = VERBALIST

Anagram Annie II

1. INSOLENT + G = SINGLETON
2. SOUVENIR + L = REVULSION
3. EMERSION + Z = SERMONIZE
4. RATIFIES + P = APERITIFS
5. DEMONIST + W = DOWNTIMES
6. QUESTION + T = QUOTIENTS
7. OVERSPIN + C = PROVINCES
8. SIDELONG + S = GODLINESS
9. ACCREDIT + P = PRACTICED
10. ETHNICAL + C = TECHNICAL
11. SCOREPAD + Y = COPYREADS
12. SOBRIETY + V = VERBOSITY
13. GASOLINE + D = ALONGSIDE
14. SERENITY + A = EYESTRAIN
15. CENTRISM + O = INTERCOMS
16. RESONANT + K = NONSKATER
17. RAFTSMEN + G = FRAGMENTS
18. SAUTERNE + M = NUMERATES
19. LINEARLY + T = RELIANTLY
20. LONELIER + B = REBELLION

Anagram PhD

1. peRcolate
2. perDition
3. puncTuate
4. patchWork
5. piggyBack
6. pregnancY
7. priVilege
8. photoCopy
9. pluraliZe
10. prOfanity
11. proXimity
12. pAtronize
13. physiQues
14. pitchFork
15. paralySis
16. paragraPh
17. pIneapple
18. psycHotic
19. paiNfully
20. pUlverize
21. preshrunK
22. prophEtic
23. paraMount
24. perJurers
25. pamphLets
26. patronaGe

Anagram PhD II

1. hyPocrite
2. homeGrown
3. horoscopE
4. honeYcomb
5. hillBilly
6. haphaZard
7. herbiCide
8. hardcoVer
9. homiciDal
10. harbInger
11. hacKneyed
12. heirlOoms
13. housewiFe
14. handiWork
15. heXagonal
16. haLitosis
17. handlebaR
18. harMonize
19. hypnotiSt
20. holocaUst
21. hierArchy
22. hisTorian
23. heartburN
24. hitchHike

Anagram PhD III

1. diversioN
2. dEfendant
3. duplicaTe
4. dAndelion
5. drumsticK
6. decaDence
7. daiQuiris
8. driftWood
9. difficuLt
10. deodoriZe
11. dallianCe
12. diFfident
13. daydreaMs
14. democRacy
15. dirigiBle
16. dormitorY
17. dIctation
18. davenpOrt
19. devaState
20. deXterity
21. detectiVe
22. dUmbbells
23. dollHouse
24. diPlomacy
25. derrinGer

Compounding the Difficulty

1. GATEWAY   GETAWAY
2. PINTAILS   TAILSPIN
3. SANDWORMS SWORDSMAN
4. DOORPOST   DOORSTOP
5. HANGOVER   OVERHANG
6. KEYNOTES   KEYSTONE
7. HOUSETOP   POTHOUSE
8. BLOWFISH   FISHBOWL

9. EELGRASS   GEARLESS
10. BOGEYMAN   MONEYBAG
11. BACKSIDE   DIEBACKS
12. SEAWEEDS   SEESAWED
13. DOWNTURN   TURNDOWN
14. OUTTAKES   TAKEOUTS   STAKEOUT   OUTSKATE
15. LAMENESS   MALENESS   NAMELESS   SALESMEN

IMAGINATIVE INGMAR

1. DODDERED
2. KICKBACK
3. NONUNION
4. REFERRER
5. ASSESSES
6. TATTIEST
7. MUUMUU
8. BOWWOW
   POWWOW
9. EULOGIA
   SEQUOIA

STUTTERING STANLEY

1. MAESTRO + GG = MORTGAGES
2. GIRLIES + ZZ = GRIZZLIES
3. ADIEU + TTT = ATTITUDE
4. SOONER + HH = SHOEHORN
5. LEFTS + OOOO = FOOTLOOSE
6. STABLE + III = ABILITIES
7. IMPACT + EEE = PEACETIME
8. STAND + YY = DYNASTY
9. STIPEND + WW = WINDSWEPT
10. COUSIN + MMM = COMMUNISM
11. STOMPS + UUU = SUMPTUOUS

STUTTERING STANLEY II

1. PLANETS + GG = EGGPLANTS
2. PEEVES + RRR = PRESERVER
3. SARDINE + PP = SANDPIPER
4. DENSELY + WW = NEWLYWEDS
5. MOUSER + TTT = UTTERMOST
6. TACKIER + BB = BACKBITER
7. STUMPIER + CCC = CIRCUMSPECT
8. STAMMER + YY = ASYMMETRY
9. PUSHER + OOO = POORHOUSE
10. INSIDES + VV = VIVIDNESS
11. TRASHES + UU = THESAURUS

ANACRYPTICS

UNDERCOVER AGENT
1. TEENAGED
2. VINTAGE
3. EGYPTIAN
4. MAGNETIC
5. GAUNTEST
6. PENTAGON
7. GNATLIKE
8. GUNMETAL
9. DOWNSTAGE, TRAGEDIAN
10. FATTENING
11. ENTOURAGE
12. NAUGHTIER
13. GENIALITY
14. GODPARENT

DEAR ONE
1. YESTERDAY
2. UNDERPAID
3. MADEIRA
4. BREADLINE
5. WARDROBE
6. PARROTED
7. WANDERER
8. ADVERTISE
9. DISAGREE
10. DEFRAUDED
11. BAREFACED
12. BELABORED
13. DOOMSAYER
14. SOREHEAD

GIRL GUIDE
1. PILGRIM
2. LINGERER
3. DARLING
4. ALLERGIES
5. FILMGOER
6. MADRIGAL
7. LONGHAIR
8. FIREPLUG
9. SLURPING
10. GRIDLOCK
11. LITTERBUG
12. RADIOLOGY
13. BULLRING
14. ALLIGATOR

HI THERE!
1. BOHEMIAN
2. HAYWIRE
3. SIDESHOW
4. LOOPHOLE
5. DOLLHOUSE
6. HELLHOLE
7. WHOLESALE
8. MOLEHILL
9. ARMCHAIR
10. ADHESIVE

YES-MAN
1. LAZYBONES
2. ODYSSEY
3. SWAYABLE, HESITANCY
4. DYSLEXIA
5. SEDENTARY
6. BLASPHEMY
7. FREESTYLE
8. DELUSORY
9. SOYBEAN
10. GUERNSEY

SPELL CHECK
1. MAX: EXAMPLE, SMALLPOX, MIXABLE, PAROXYSMS, REEXAMINED
2. MARY: AMARYLLIS, SYCAMORE, MONETARY, REPAYMENT, READYMADE
3. TIM: ANTIWOMAN, COSMETIC, ALTIMETERS, BOMBSIGHTS, WARTIME, PEACETIME

4. JOE: FOREJUDGE, JOBHOLDER, JOYRIDER, ADJOURNED, PROJECTED
5. SETH: THERAPIST, HYGIENIST, ATHLETICS, BEDSHEETS, NORTHWEST
6. MAY: ANONYMOUS, AMICABLY, TEMPORARY, DAYDREAM, PLAYMATE, PALIMONY
7. JIM: JASMINE, BENJAMIN, JUMPSUIT, MARIJUANA, MAJORITY, MAJESTIES
8. DAN: HACKNEYED, LAUNCHED, HEADWINDS, BALLOONED, DISTANCE, DANGEROUS
9. ANN: ANCHORMAN, SENSATIONAL, INSURANCE, KIDNAPPING, ABUNDANT, HANGINGS
10. MIKE: MARKETING, MAVERICK, FILMMAKERS, GIMMICKED, DREAMLIKE

LETTER PATTERNS

CIRCULAR VISION
1. UTOPIA
2. NAUSEA
3. NYMPHS
4. ALKALI
5. AERIAL
6. AVIATE
7. DYNAMO
8. OINKED
9. ESCAPE
10. ENVIED
11. ERADICATED
12. INTERFERER
13. REMUNERATE
14. MEMORANDUM
15. EUCALYPTUS
16. CRESCENDOS
17. APOSTROPHE
18. CITRONELLA
19. YESTERYEAR
20. REJUVENATE

CIRCULAR VISION II
1. FORSYTHE
2. BONIFACE
3. ADENAUER
4. AUGUSTUS
5. COUSTEAU
6. KHOMEINI
7. PAGANINI
8. ZIEGFELD

CIRCULAR VISION III
1. TENNYSON
2. VESPUCCI
3. THATCHER
4. RONSTADT
5. NIJINSKY
6. GILLETTE
7. ROCKWELL
8. DIETRICH

CIRCULAR VISION IV
1. DIOGENES
2. CRONKITE
3. BEAUVOIR
4. BREZHNEV
5. IGLESIAS
6. SCHUBERT
7. HUMPHREY
8. CARNEGIE

Switcheroo

1. EMPHATIC
2. LAMBSKIN
3. CACKLING
4. SLUMBER
5. TOPPINGS
6. SINGLING
7. TRUSTIES
8. LOWDOWNS
9. STATELESS
10. DISCRETELY
11. ODORLESS
12. NAMEABLE
13. SUABILITY
14. OVERDOSE
15. PRETEENS
16. COMPLIANT
17. BLANKETS
18. RUSTICLY
19. ALTITUDE
20. TRIDENTS
21. COMPADRE
22. COTILLION
23. INSISTER
24. SIMMERED
25. GEOCENTRIC
26. CASUALLY
27. OVERBUSY
28. ARMOIRES
29. FATBACKS
30. HATCHETS

Switcheroo II

1. CHAGRIN
2. MINUET
3. PREMIES
4. GLUIEST
5. VENEER
6. MANATEE
7. VENERATE
8. SUNROOF
9. BRASSIER
10. REPENTED
11. PRIMROSE
12. FREIGHTS
13. PSALMIST
14. STARRIER
15. RANCHO
16. PIGEON
17. INKLING
18. WHOEVER
19. EDIFIED
20. CUTLET
21. EARTHIER
22. WENCHERS
23. PROGENY
24. EARLIEST
25. VILENESS
26. STRUMPET
27. TRICKLE
28. SPILLAGE
29. CHARIOT
30. DISSEVER

WORD PATTERNS

Middleman

1. FORENOON
2. ROUTEWAY
3. SPHINXES
4. HOMOGENY
5. GRIMACED
6. LIKEABLE
7. TANGIBLE
8. GRATUITY
9. OUTYELL
10. FLAVOR
11. URETHRA
12. GEARBOX
13. ARABIZED
14. PABULUMS
15. DUELLER
16. SEXISMS
17. SPILLWAY

Middleman II

1. ARTICHOKE
2. BAZOOKA
3. DECORUM
4. BOURBON
5. MONOGRAM
6. ANTELOPE
7. INCISOR
8. BOGEYMAN
9. OREGANOS
10. BIOPSIES
11. SAUCEPAN
12. TELETHON
13. TOWAWAY
14. WAKEFUL
15. JETLINER
16. AMPUTATED
17. UNMOLTEN

CLOAK AND DAGGER
1. VICTIMHOOD : In My Humble Opinion
2. BEVERAGE : Earned Run Average; Equal Rights Amendment
3. EFFICACY : Federal Insurance Contributions Act
4. ANATOMIES : North Atlantic Treaty Organization
5. DOWNRANGE : Nation Rifle Association; National Recovery Administration
6. BEANBAG : National Basketball Association; National Boxing Association
7. CROTCHETY : Reserve Officers' Training Corps
8. SCARECROW : Cooperative for American Relief to Everywhere
9. ENSWATHE : Special Weapons and Tactics
10. NASALLY : National Aeronautics and Space Administration
11. SEATMATE : Automated Teller Machine
12. OLIGOPOLY : Grand Old Party
13. SPECIAL : Central Intelligence Agency
14. SHOPTALK : Parent-Teacher Association
15. ODDSMAKER : Doctor of Dental Science (or Surgery)

CLOAK AND DAGGER II
1. POPCORN : Personal Computer; Peace Corps; Percent; Politically Correct
2. GUNFLINT : National Football League
3. ZESTY : Eastern Standard Time
4. OPINION : Personal Identification Number
5. ASEPTIC : Simplified Employee Pension
6. POSTCODE : Collect (or Cash) On Delivery
7. GUARD : United Arab Republic
8. CHOWHOUND : World Health Organization
9. GENDARME : Daughters of the American Revolution
10. HUMDRUM : Medical Doctor; Maryland; Muscular Dystrophy
11. NONOWNER : National Organization for Women
12. UNIFYING : For Your Information
13. MAUSOLEUM : United Service Organizations
14. HAPLOID : Palestine Liberation Organization
15. MARSUPIAL : United Press International

NOT VERY EASY PUZZLE
1. parsley
2. embassy
3. nosegay
4. wayside
5. assembly
6. sprayer

7. rosemary
8. grayness
9. seminary
10. overstay
11. mastery
12. loyalties
13. jealousy
14. amethyst
15. yeastier
16. ancestry
17. eyestrain
18. syndicate
19. typecast
20. accessory
21. horseplay
22. yesterday
23. passerby
24. saleslady

Quite a Hard Puzzle

1. radish
2. orchard
3. hayride
4. hairdo
5. verandah
6. redhead
7. philander
8. cheddars
9. authored
10. daughter
11. dishware
12. discharge
13. birthday
14. unheard
15. fathered
16. shipyard
17. foolhardy
18. arrowhead
19. hydraulic
20. cardsharp
21. dehydrate
22. watershed
23. underhand
24. dashboard

Really Tough Puzzle

1. drought
2. staghound
3. shotguns
4. hangout
5. toughie
6. yoghurt
7. autograph
8. outgrowth
9. although
10. grouchiest
11. houseguest
12. overbought
13. bigmouth
14. outright
15. doughnut
16. roughest
17. thorough

Trivia and Word Meanings

Thespians

1. ETHICIANS
2. MORTICIAN
3. LIBRARIAN
4. SIMIAN
5. AQUARIAN
6. MERIDIAN
7. AMPHIBIAN
8. REPTILIAN
9. DALMATIAN
10. PATRICIAN
11. COLLEGIANS
12. TRAGEDIANS

Colorful Speech

1. green thumb
2. whitewash
3. blue flu
4. red-light district
5. brown shirt
6. yellow pages
7. red-bait
8. white knight
9. Bluebeard
10. greenhorn
11. black belt
12. Golden Rule
13. Orangemen
14. red tape
15. silver screen
16. pink elephants
17. Golden Fleece
18. rose-colored glasses

Colorful Speech II
1. red ink
2. silver bullet
3. gold digger
4. pink lady
5. goldbrick
6. gray matter
7. blackjack
8. yellow-dog contract
9. white-bread
10. red-blooded
11. black hole
12. green-eyed monster
13. white elephant
14. black sheep
15. yellow journalism
16. blackmail

Language Shape-Up
1. Lone Star State
2. Oval Office
3. stardust
4. round-robin
5. square one
6. (New York) Times Square
7. Bermuda Triangle
8. pyramid scheme
9. traffic circles
10. Roundhead
11. square shooter
12. love triangle
13. star of Bethelem
14. roundhouse
15. sewing circle

Transformers
1. secret, secretary
2. pole, polemic
3. arch, archeology
4. comb, combatant
5. pun, puncture
6. Bach, bachelor
7. stag, stagehand
8. rein, reincarnation
9. dog, doggerel
10. bear, beardless

Transformers II
1. read, readjust
2. plan, plantation
3. slot, slothful
4. bell, bellyache
5. papa, paparazzo
6. disco, discomfort
7. coin, coincidence
8. dive, divestiture
9. extra, extravagant
10. doc, documentary

Transformers III
1. class, classified
2. dim, dimension
3. car, caricature
4. den, denizen
5. pen, penitentiary
6. père, perennial
7. rat, rationalization
8. sub, subterfuge
9. ski, skirmish
10. par, parentheses

LARRY AND DIANE'S DIVERSIONS

DIANE'S DECEPTIVE DIARY

1. Ingrid
2. Bradley
3. Ricardo
4. Marianne
5. Laurel
6. Irving
7. Lindsey
8. Bertha
9. Carmine
10. Dwayne
11. Maurice
12. Doreen
13. Thelma
14. Glenda
15. Rodney
16. Tabitha
17. Melissa
18. Nicolas
19. Laurence
20. Theresa
21. Pascale
22. Cornelius
23. Rosetta
24. Reginald
25. Alonso
26. Geraldine
27. Rosalind
28. Isabella
29. Esther, Hester
30. Arnold, Roland, Ronald

Super Snoop Credit: Dorothea, Theodora

LITERAL LARRY'S TRAVELOG

1. Lagos
2. Limoges
3. Yugoslavia
4. Long Island
5. Monongahela
6. Los Angeles
7. Mongolia
8. Portugal
9. Golgotha
10. Galápagos Islands or Archipiélago de Colón
11. Glasgow
12. Volga
13. Golden Gate
14. Colorado Springs, Colorado

LITERAL LARRY'S TWO-TIMERS

1. couscous
2. muumuu, lavalava
3. BB or beebee, dumdum
4. pompom
5. mahimahi, tartar sauce
6. tsetse fly
7. beriberi
8. cancan, go-go
9. chowchow, chow chow
10. atlatl
11. chichi, froufrou
12. juju
13. dodo
14. pawpaw
15. nene
16. wa-wa or wahwah
17. tom-tom or tam-tam

LITERAL LARRY'S CROSSWORDS

1. papyrus Playboy
2. iceberg inkblot
3. morphin mudpack
4. vampire vanpool
5. windchill wisecrack
6. hunchback hatchback

LITERAL LARRY'S CROSSWORDS II

1. barmaid boombox
2. colleen collard
3. gondola gumdrop
4. Jughead jodhpur
5. bluegrass bodyguard
6. Skywalker marmalade

ABOUT THE AUTHORS

RITA NORR is the 1987 National Scrabble® Champion [the ONLY woman ever to hold the title], the 1993 and 1994 Long Island Champion, and was listed in the *Guinness Book of World Records*. She was a member of the U.S. team for the second World Scrabble® Championship in New York (1993) and the third World Scrabble® Championship in London (1995). She has a bachelor's in computer science. She is married, has three children and a golden retriever named Max, and lives in Connecticut.

AUDREY TUMBARELLO is an expert-ranked Scrabble® player, rated 45th in the United States in 1996. She has a bachelor's in American literature and is currently a College Now program coordinator for Kingsborough Community College at the High School of Telecommunication Arts and Technology, Brooklyn, New York. She is married and has four children and one and a half grandchildren. An educational activist, she most recently served on the New York City Board of Education Curriculum Frameworks Committee and coauthored the parent section of the board's Writing Initiative.

Ms. Norr and Ms. Tumbarello are coauthors of *The Literate Puzzler*, another Sterling book.

INDEX

Answer pages are in italics.